WHEN THE PIE
WAS OPENED

*   *
   *

WHEN THE PIE WAS OPENED

* *
*

Poems by Jean Little

Little, Brown and Company
BOSTON   TORONTO

LIBRARY OF CONGRESS CATALOG CARD NO. 68–11112

FIRST EDITION

Published simultaneously in Canada
by Little, Brown & Company (Canada) Limited

PRINTED IN THE UNITED STATES OF AMERICA

For Margery

*   *
*

Contents

* *
*

When the Pie Was Opened ix

THE EQUINOX, THE FOSSIL AND THE ROSE

Are We Kidding? 3
Rain 4
Poetry's Miracle 5
Spring 6
In Passing 7
Incomparable 8
Autumn 9

TWO DOGS WAITING

Two Dogs Waiting 13
Terriers 15
The Wicked Old Woman and the Gay Young Blade
    or, Portrait of Two Dogs 16
Why Dogs? 18
I Have a Dog 19

MOSTLY A RIDDLE

The End, the Beginning and the Middle 25
As the Hive Holds the Honey 27
In Retrospect 28
Triolets for Patsy 29
Love Came Riding 32

Vacancy   36

Silence Is a Wall   37

You Reach Out to Me   38

A Friendship Is a Fragile Thing   41

THE SELF I SEE

Maybe   45

Plenty   47

Ode to the Medium Day   48

Communicating   49

But That I . . .   50

The Glory   52

THE LOVELY LAND

The Lovely Land   57

On Seeing a Leaf House   59

For My Father   60

The Knowing One   64

She Was a Clothier's Daughter   65

Homecoming   68

Worlds Within   70

To a Twelve-Year-Old Trying on Dresses   73

To the Mothers and Fathers Who Hover . . .   74

A Child   76

Listen . . . It Is a Poem   80

Tonight I Must Sing   82

When the Pie Was Opened

*   *
*

"The birds began to sing"
— So the rhyme goes.
But what they found to sing about,
Nobody knows.

Your heart's full of sky
When you're brought up with wings
And the bloom and the branch
Are what every bird sings.

These songbirds were snared though
No orchard gust
Would reach a bird buried
Beneath upper crust.

Both kitchen and courtroom
Would cage like gilt bars
When you'd spun somersaults
In the space between stars.

Those twenty-four poets,
They noticed no king.
They sang just because
It was in them to sing.

THE EQUINOX, THE FOSSIL
AND THE ROSE

*   *
*

Are We Kidding?

*   *
*

Nature was wild when we found her
  but we tamed her with names,
The equinox, the fossil and the rose.
We pickled protozoa and labeled in Latin
  anything capable of dying.
We invited apes into our history
  and we assembled the bones of Brontosaurus.
We caught birdsong on a tape recorder,
  put lions in zoos
  and mapped the weather.
Now — in LIVING COLOR
  on your CINESCANNA SCREEN
You can watch a picture — flowering.

Go on, somebody.
Why don't you change a season?

Rain

Rain is as mischief-making as a child.
She pokes the Thunder's ribs until he roars.
She sits on steepled roofs and thrums her heels
And tickles grass and taps at solemn doors.

She dampens dignitaries and their wives,
Paints saucy freckle-faces on the roads,
Makes mud puddles and rainbows; then gets down
To scrub the tiny blissful backs of toads.

Poetry's Miracle

*   *

*

The woods where Robert Frost drew rein
To watch the snow drift down
May have been felled and hauled long since
To make room for a town.

Here is poetry's miracle:
Though the trees are gone,
The woods stay "lovely, dark and deep."
The snow falls on and on.

The little horse still shakes his bells
And in the beginning night
A man still searches his heart for words,
Quiet enough and white.

Spring

*   *

*

Spring means waking in a world of wonder,
>   The first far rumble of April thunder,
Crocuses whether or not it's snowing,
>   Snowdrops sturdily, starrily growing,
A prickle of grass, sap in the trees,
>   Pussy willows and anemones,
A robin of course, plump, scarlet-chested,
>   Hunting up a wife and getting nested,
Forsythia like sunshine turned into flowers,
>   Over-in-a-minute pell-mell showers,
A tadpole, a tulip, skipping rhymes and ropes,
>   A boy with three marbles — and enormous hopes,
Waking in the morning with the sun in your face,
>   Grasshoppers, daffodils all over the place,
The scent of lilacs sweetening the dark,
>   Seesaws and swings going up in the park,
Mosquitoes beginning, worms in a can,
>   Office girls starting on their Sunday tan,
Dandelions too new yet to be weeds,
>   Crisp colored envelopes of small brown seeds,
Shedding snowpants, wool scarves, mittens,
>   A tumble of puppies, a clamber of kittens,
The smell of the earth warming into life,
>   Orchards run riot, gardens gone rife
With blossom and birdsong, a crow's harsh cry,
>   Then, one small silken butterfly.

. . . It is older than Eden, yet endlessly new.
No matter how often Spring happens to you,
It comes suddenly, shining and sweet as the first.
Spring means miracles unrehearsed.

In Passing

*   *
*

A quail walked calmly through our vacant lot,
Dipping his head to eat, swinging his plume.
His serenity turned weeds to flowers
And made the city give him elbowroom.

Incomparable

*   *
*

Chalk, the flesh of apples, gulls' wings, pearls,
Egg whites beaten stiff in a china bowl,
Sheets ironed smooth, steamed rice, a winter moon,
The incandescence of a shriven soul,

Any image that comes to light the mind
When the word "white" is spoken or thought by man,
A quire of paper, lilies, linen, clouds —
New snow is whiter than.

Autumn

* *
*

The spine of autumn is reality.
Trees strip to bark and fields lay bare their earth.
Rubble is burned to ash. In honest dearth,
The land awaits the frost. Identity

Emerges from the summer's bright disguise.
Black and austere, the branches take the days
Nor shift before the candor of my gaze.
From their poised nakedness, I drop my eyes.

The leaves, which once were bracelets for these boughs,
Fall to the gutter, rattle and are still.
Music and color flee. The ravaged hill
Is left with bulk alone to meet the snows.

All life is disciplined by nature's rule.
Even sapient man she does not spare.
We too slough our external flesh and hair
And feel our skeletons, composed and cool.

Insight is given as we find it good
To know there is a purpose in our bones,
To learn that, even robbed of shades and tones,
A part remains. Autumn is understood.

Better can we withstand the coming storm
When we possess this knowledge of a core
With its endurance measured, known for more
Than any wind can ruin — clear, stark form.

The spine of autumn is reality.
Then shed we all our various veneers
And see, behind the practiced tricks and tears,
Each separate and brave integrity.

TWO DOGS WAITING

* *
*

Two Dogs Waiting

* *
*

I'll comfort you with apples
Or an upstairs maid,
A plum tree, a ball gown
Stiff with brocade.

Tell me of the treasure
You cannot resist.
Would you like a nugget
As big as your fist?

A doll's house? A tea rose?
A carriage and four?
A genuine horseshoe
To hang above your door?

I'll make you a melody
Upon my guitar.
I'll give you a skipping rope,
I'll steal you a star.

Champagne or cider?
A mountain? A sea?
A week in Spain? An aeroplane?
A cup of hot tea?

I will give you castles,
Or Chippendale chairs,
Or two dogs waiting
At the top of the stairs.

Keep the maid, the apples,
The star you stole for me,
The rose and the nugget,
The song and the sea.

Keep the gown, the doll's house,
The carriage and four,
And you may hang the horseshoe
Above your own door.

I couldn't cope with castles,
The mountain you may keep,
The former would be draughty,
The latter too steep.

Keep the rope for skipping,
And the white plum tree,
The champagne, the cider,
The trip to Spain, the tea.

Even keep the aeroplane
And antique chairs,
But leave me the two dogs
Waiting on the stairs.

Terriers

* *
  *

Poodles go prancing on pedicured paws.
Setters are fleet as a song.
Wolfhounds stalk haughtily. Corgis cavort.
But terriers trundle along.

Cockers have amber eyes limpid with love.
Collies look tragic and wise.
A Labrador's gaze is benignly adult
But you can't find a terrier's eyes.

Some dogs are mammoth and some are minute.
A Peke you can pocket with ease
While a Saint Bernard stands as high as your waist.
Terriers just come to your knees.

All dogs are watchdogs. A dog worth his salt
His home and his hearthfire defends.
He'll bark at a burglar, or breadman or boy!
But terriers growl at their friends.

Some dogs have beauty and some dogs have brains.
Tricks some are capable of.
There are show dogs and sheepdogs and gun dogs and guides.
But terriers know about love.

The Wicked Old Woman
and the Gay Young Blade,

or

Portrait of Two Dogs

* *
*

Susie is the wicked old woman.
Robbie is the gay young blade.
She says to him, "You young idiot!"
She grabs his ball and warns him away.
She charges him from behind and knocks him flat.
"You young whippersnapper," she grumbles.
"Out of my way," she tells him.

Susie is the boss and the bully.
Robbie is the darling and the clown.
She shoulders him away from the water dish.
She orders me to stop scratching his head.
When he wants to play, she mentions her arthritis.
When he wants to share the couch,
She glares at him over the edge and threatens terrible things.
He whimpers and retreats under the footstool.
She turns her back and pretends to go to sleep.

Susie is the grown-up dog, the first one.
Robbie is the baby still, the pup.

When he is downcast enough, when he has learned some
  manners,
She gives the tennis ball a poke with her paw.
It rolls like magic right in front of his nose.
She lies quite still and watches him dart away.

He's always wanting out. (She never goes
Unless she has business requiring her attention.)
But if I forget him in favor of my book,
"Come!" she calls frantically. "Hurry! The baby wants in!"
She hustles me out to the door. I let him in.
She cuffs him soundly the moment he steps inside.
. . . "What can I DO?" he whines. "There's nothing to do!"
She throws away five years and roars "You're IT."
. . . "I'm lonely," he cries. "Nobody loves me." Then
She, who has never had a pup of her own,
Moves over and lets him share her patch of sun.
"Don't be silly," she tells him. "I'm right here."

Why Dogs?

*   *
*

People who live doglessly
Remain a mystery to me.
Dogs, several or singular,
Help you discover who you are,
And then dogs, courteous and kind,
Help you to live with what you find.

I Have a Dog

*   *
*

I have a dog
Who's growing old.
Her joints are stiff.
She's prone to scold.

When she was young,
She raced. Of late,
Her pace has slowed.
She is sedate.

She trailed me like
A friendly spy,
But now that she's
Become less spry,

She lets me start
And waits to see
If I'll return
Immediately.

If I do not
Come back to her,
She sighs and sets
Herself astir.

Like Sherlock Holmes,
She sniffs about —

And every time
She finds me out.

She wags; then stretches
Out where she
Can keep a watchful
Eye on me.

I've often told her
"Rest now. Stay.
You need not dog
My steps this way."

She understands —
But pays no heed.
She comprehends
My deeper need.

Although involved
To point of stress,
I'm haunted by
Life's loneliness.

I'm caught off guard
By black despair.
I reach for love,
And find none there —

Until my dog
Comes after me
And demonstrates
Love's constancy.

My dog is old.
In time, the breath
Within her will
Be stilled by death.

And I shall vainly
Listen for
The pad of paws
Along the floor.

She will no longer
Shake off sleep,
Her love to prove,
Her charge to keep.

How will I with
My fears contend,
Robbed of the comfort
Of this friend?

Life is a stormy
Adversary.
Having been wounded,
I am wary

And apt to turn
From love's clear call
And hide my hurts
Behind a wall.

I have a dog
Who's old and lame.

I only have
To speak her name

To set her foolish
Tail in motion
And win a look
Of dog-devotion.

My dog would not
Win Best in Show.
She's shaggy, grubby,
Stout and slow.

She's not a great
Philosopher.
The gift of love
Was born in her.

And yet in sober
Hope, I pray
That when she dies
I somehow may

Learn to love life
As she loves me,
With valor and
Fidelity.

MOSTLY A RIDDLE

* *
*

The End, the Beginning and the Middle

*　　*
*

Love that is ending
Is no use defending,
Long past repairing,
Wounding, wearing.

Do not spend hours,
　　Denying, appealing.
Love is a whole,
　　Not a half-hearted feeling.

Let it go cleanly,
　　And stand you free,
Play the jester,
　　In gay motley.

Love is for making,
　　Rather than mending,
Deliver yourself,
　　From love that is ending.

Yet love just beginning,
Is worthy the winning,
The making a start on,
The risking your heart on.

However embittered,
　　No matter how scarred,

Cease to be wary,
    Lower your guard.

Let it come lightly,
    And clothe you in
Radiance, rapture,
    Without, within.

Bravely, unstintingly,
    Heels-over-hearting,
Surrender yourself
    To love that is starting.

Love in the middle
Is mostly a riddle,
To work at, to live for,
To trust in and give for.

Do not list failings
    Or look for a cause
Love is illogical.
    Love's full of flaws.

Live in it fully
    And learn its art,
Involve your mind
    And commit your heart.

Give and take joyously.
    Grumbling or glowing,
Believe in, belong to,
    Love that is growing.

As the Hive Holds the Honey

* *

*

As the hive holds the honey,
As the cage holds the dove,
As the mint holds money,
My heart holds love.

As the road loves the rover,
As the bird loves the blue,
As the cow loves clover,
My heart loves you.

While my head holds a story,
While my heart holds a song,
While my hand holds a pencil,
I'll love you that long,

Through bliss and through boredom,
Through singing and sorrow,
Through all my todays
And through every tomorrow.

In Retrospect

*   *

*

I thought our love was meat and drink,
Daylight and a charm
I wore around my heart to keep
Me safe from harm.

I thought that if it were to end
Life would be finished too
For in those days the sun came up
Because of you.

I never guessed how frail a thing
I was enamored of
Until I roused and saw the true
Dimensions of our love.

You claimed my heart held just one room,
Its every cranny yours,
But now I find my heart to be
A castle full of doors.

I fling them wide on every side
And praise God I am free
From love which seemed so vast a thing
Yet proved so niggardly.

Triolets for Patsy

* *
*

A triolet's queer.
It looks easy to do
But that's really unfair
For a triolet's queer.
It rhymes everywhere.
I wrote some for you.
A triolet's queer.
It looks easy to do.

I long for the day
When my sister will come.
We have so much to say.
I long for the day.
She has been far away
But she soon will be home.
I long for the day
When my sister will come.

My sister is here
With her daughter, her son.
It is crowded and queer.
My sister is here
But the hours disappear
And our talk's not begun.
My sister is here
With her daughter, her son.

My sister has gone,
Her visit was good.
It was not like my plan.
My sister has gone
With our talk still undone,
But we loved as we should.
My sister has gone.
Her visit was good.

That our love stay the same
Is the heart of the matter.
I am glad that she came,
That our love stays the same,
Sweet as bread, bright as flame.
We have no need to chatter.
That our love stay the same
Is the heart of the matter.

Now I plan for a day
That waits somewhere ahead.
She has gone far away,
But I plan for the day
When she'll come and we'll say
All the things left unsaid.
Now I plan for a day
That waits somewhere ahead.

If these plans go awry,
Still our loving is sure.
Though the hours hurry by,
Though these plans go awry,
We shall laugh, she and I,
And our love will endure.
If these plans go awry,
Still our loving is sure.

I shall write to her now
With my heart in each word.
Of books and the snow
I shall write to her now.
When she reads it, I know
That my love will be heard.
I shall write to her now
With my heart in each word.

Love Came Riding

*　　*
*

On a golden morning
In the world's beginning,
Love stood in a garden,
Legendary, fair.
Eve, surprised by living,
Wakened in a green glade,
Wakened to a world — but saw
Only Adam there.

Once upon a blue noon,
Love sang "Tirralirra."
Love came on his high horse
Down the river road.
On his milk-white charger
(Or his coal-black stallion)
Love went by her window —
And the morning glowed.

Down the moonlit highway,
Love came riding, riding,
Dressed up like a dandy
With lace at throat and wrist.
Like Eve before her,
Like the girl who hurried
To dare fate at her window,
Bess could not resist.

In a misty twilight,
Miss Eyre walked out primly,
Walked to mail a letter
Through the dusk alone,
And Love, once more, came riding,
Love, hell-bent and reckless —
Into Jane's sedate life
Rochester was thrown.

Miss Eliza Bennett
Met with Mr. D'Arcy,
Found him downright snobbish,
Left him strangely vexed.
But Love said "Please forgive me."
"God bless you, Miss Elizabeth."
Wedding bells set pealing
Were what happened next.

Ruth looked up at Boaz —
And faltered in her gleaning.
Rachel blushed when Jacob
Approached her by the well.
Guenevere was faithless
And Juliet was forward —
What made her man different
Not one of them could tell.

Except his armor glistened,
Except his eyes were lonely,
Except he wore a cocked hat,
Except, till then, no one
Had made bells ring inside her,
Had made her heartbeat stammer,
Had made a sudden brightness
More dazzling than the sun.

The poets help you feel it:
The shock, the fixed stars reeling,
The breathlessness, the searching
For trivial words to say.
Love came then on a high horse,
With swirling cloak and dagger.
Love scaled walls, spoke in poems —
Does he exist today?

Love — in a football sweater?
Sir Lancelot — in blue jeans?
Romeo — in gray flannel
Or serviceable tweed!
Where is the spice, the danger,
The brooding, brilliant stranger,
The burst of bells, the blazing day?
Gone is Love indeed.

Yet Lancelot was never
The only knight in armor.
Men clad in burnished metal
Were all his ladies knew.
At the ball Mercutio
Was equally mysterious.
To the Inn came others
Sporting cocked hats too.

Love stands out at a party.
Love strolls into the office.
Love shares your hymnbook with you,
And in that moment he
Is Lancelot and Adam
And Romeo and D'Arcy
And all the rest who sometime
Made bells chime inwardly.

Vacancy

*   *
   *

I do not love you any more,
My heart is now To Let
Although I still must make myself
Remember to forget.

It seemed so real, so right, our love,
So very nearly true.
But faced with "almost," I was forced
To close my heart to you.

I only hope, before too long,
The day will come for me
When I stop feeling faithless
And start feeling free.

Silence Is a Wall

*   *
*

Silence is a wall.
Although we sit together,
We are each alone.

Silence lies between.
Say "Spring will soon be with us."
Reach me with your words.

And I shall reply,
"Today I saw a crocus
Poking through the snow."

Love is like a gate.
Before we can walk through it,
We must lift the latch.

You Reach Out to Me

* *
*

You reach out to me,
   and yet your hand
Can never stretch
   to where I now stand.

You speak, but no word
   has ever crossed
To this aloneness
   where I am lost.

They are missing here,
   the song of the bird,
The scent of the rose,
   the warmth of a word.

Here there is only
   the enemy,
A foe I would that
   I could not see.

Despair and his host
   surround this place,
And every one of them
   wears my face.

Within myself,
   our war goes on.

Within myself,
  the lines are drawn.

I defend a love
  that I used to feel.
I fight for a life
  that once was real.

Save for the memory
  of them,
I have no armor,
  no stratagem.

From the start it is plain
  that I must yield.
Most of my force
  has fled the field.

A twist of laughter,
  a trace of will,
A dogged endurance
  stay with me still.

And a touch unfelt
  and a voice unheard,
Your reaching hand,
  your steadying word.

Thus allied,
  I will not retreat
I stand my ground,
  I deny defeat.

Obviously,
    this frail defense
Is sheer bravado,
    is mere pretense.

Yet, for no cause
    I can define,
My enemy
    calls back his line.

He does not grant me
    the victory,
But, for a season,
    he sets me free.

Living and love
    once more mean much.
Words come through again.
    Fingers touch.

Still, I treasure most
    the touch, the speech
Which reached me
    when I was out of reach.

This is a strange return,
    it's true,
The desert within
    I have shown to you.

Yet I've told the aloneness
    which can't be told
And here is my nothingness
    to hold.

40

A Friendship Is a Fragile Thing

*   *
*

A friendship is a fragile thing
Like the dust of bloom on a butterfly's wing.
Presuming on it is like trying
To keep a butterfly from flying.
You cup your hands, try not to clutch,
But it is crippled by your touch,
By all the self-involved demands
Implicit in your closing hands.
Though friendship may stay acquiescent,
It is no longer iridescent.
There is no way man can contrive
To catch its loveliness alive
And keep it in captivity.
To glow, love must have liberty.
Yes, friendship is a fragile thing
Like the dust of bloom on a butterfly's wing.

Yet, deep in love there also lies
The bravery of butterflies.
Butterflies go through nights of storm
Migrating to a land that's warm.
They drift in brilliant frailty,
Testaments to mortality,
And all the while they own the strength
To mount the wind and come at length

Home again, their loveliness
Enduring through the journey's stress.
A treasured friendship also can
Survive the blunderings of man.
Although it is a fragile thing,
It has the courage to take wing,
Dare to ride the dark and come
Bravely home.

THE SELF I SEE

*   *

*

Maybe

* *
*

When I was a microscopic egg,
    infinitesimal and unaware,
My mother gave me a tipped-up nose
    and my father donated fairish hair.
As early as that, inexorably,
They hedged me in with heredity.

And now you tell me that, since my birth,
    the books I read, my church, my friends
Are molding me, whether I will or no,
    are shaping me to their various ends.
Those traits in me which are not parental
I must categorize as "environmental."

So what, I say. So what! So what!
    If I have no hand in making me,
Still, I exist. And, what is more,
    I am not repulsed by the self I see.
While I can live with me undismayed,
I refuse to begrudge the way I'm made.

And a day may arrive, as yet, you know,
    when I'll leave all the molders in the lurch,
When I'll start reading some other books
    and dye my hair and change my church.
I'll call myself by a different name
None of my friends will stay the same.

I'll turn into something you hadn't meant
And leave you wondering where I went.

I can't say I'm planning to yet, but still,
Maybe, one of these days, I will!

Plenty

*   *
*

I have plenty of everything
  but want.
I try to imagine hunger,
Try to believe that I have not eaten today,
That I must stand in line for a bowl of soup,
That my cheekbones angle out of my hollowed face;
But I smell the roast in the oven.
I hear the laden refrigerator hum.

I think of people whose walls are made of wind.
I stand outside in the cold.
I tell myself I am homeless and dressed in rags;
But my shiver lacks conviction.
I stand in fleece-lined boots and winter coat.
Home is a block away.

I leave my wallet at home.
Pretending I have no money,
I walk past stores and wish.
"I have no money, no money at all, no money —"
I turn my head in shame as I pass the bank.

I pay for a parcel of food. I gather clothes.
I adopt a child under a foster parent plan.
I do what I can. I am generous. I am kind —

I still have plenty of everything
  but want.

Ode to the Medium Day

*   *
*

I celebrate the medium day,
   Neither gay nor sad,
When nothing is too beautiful
   To bear nor yet too bad.

When crises are of moderate size
   And come in single file,
When I've no reason to rejoice
   But sense enough to smile,

The peaceful day, the pleasant day,
   The day that's ordinary,
The settled day that would not dare
   Abruptly veer or vary,

When I have room to breathe, when I
   Can call my soul my own,
When I'm allowed at least one hour
   Entirely alone,

The day when I pay bills, write books,
   Sort clothes, get letters penned,
The day when I have time to spare
   As well as time to spend.

I celebrate the medium day
　　When I can get things done.
I only wish that heaven would
　　See fit to send me one!

Communicating

*　　*
　*

Communicating's more than merely talking.
Communicating's when a thing unsaid
Is heard and shared and given deeper meaning.
It's like good bread

And cheese. Now either, by itself, is splendid
And yet, when you combine and taste the two,
They add to one another a fresh flavor.
The same is true

Of minds that meet and match. There's something extra,
A gleam, a swiftness neither knew before.
Talking stays in one room. Communicating
Opens the door.

But That I . . .

*   *
*

I believe in death:
the old woman dying minute by minute,
her palsied, spotted hands and rusty voice
fumbling among her ragbag, rattletrap thoughts.
She used to go barefoot and sing solos
and once,
she smiled and dwelt on her brightness in a mirror.
No one has called her Janie now
for thirty years.

I believe
in the young wife tragically murmured about,
cancer eating her bones,
consuming her casual tomorrows.

And I believe
in the motorcycle thundering into fragments
against the inexorable tree.

I believe in all the
headlines;
the quake, the crash, the landslide, the assassin —
the hundred, thousand strangers without life.

But that I,
that I will not be here
to smell the lilacs,
open doors, climb stairs —
that I shall lie
numb bones, or even
somewhere enlarge my existence
while unknown others breakfast, read through
   Dickens,
watch the snow fall
or simply walk these streets,
accepting as theirs the birdsong and the sunset —
This is clearly impossible, past belief,
Even though I understand it will happen.

The Glory

*   *
  *

The room I had lived in all my life,
Was lit by candlelight.
If ever that flame went out, I knew
There would be only night.

Sometimes I blew on it, cautiously,
And watched it flicker, but then,
Afraid of the dark, I held my breath
Till it burned tall again.

Here was the glory, the light of the world —
But what if I put it out?
Aware of the everlasting night,
I dared not test my doubt.

I bolted the door against the dark.
I kept all the blinds drawn.
And still, in the gloom of my being's room,
That steadfast candle shone.

My mother, my father both walked outside
Calmly every day,
But, whenever they opened the door, I turned
And looked the other way.

"Come," they said to me — but I stayed,
Imprisoned in childish fright.

Yet, under the drawn window blind,
I glimpsed a line of light.

They knew something I did not know.
I longed to learn it too.
But what if they had been fooled? What if
They only dreamed they knew?

Then yesterday, oh yesterday,
I opened the door up wide.
I stood on the step. I saw the sun.
I saw the light outside.

They had tried to tell me, but all their words
Had not thus dazzled my eyes.
I needed to see for myself. I saw
And wonder stilled surprise.

Here was the glory, the radiant source,
Tremendously true and free,
The night I had dreaded uncovering,
The darkness had been in me.

I remembered my candle after that —
Now need for it had passed.
I would open my life to the glory of God,
I would walk in the light at last.

Then, turning to snuff its flame, I saw
That all God's fire is one,
My parents had simply set alight
My candle from their sun.

The Lovely Land

*   *
*

When I was small, I dreamed there lay somewhere
A kingdom where each day came fresh and fair
And I could not be wrong or sad. I planned
To spend a halcyon adulthood there.

But I was small and slow to understand.
I knew not how to seek my lovely land.
A maze of unmarked roads bewildered me
Until I thought to take my father's hand.

He led the child I was so carefully
Through niceties of ethics, subtlety
Of wit. I giant-stepped to match his stride.
When we reached books, he smiled and set me free.

Always, he taught, I must myself decide
When and how far to trust in any guide.
Cocksure at times, I struck out on my own —
Knowing one word would bring him to my side.

But then, he died. I shrank from the unknown.
I who had thought myself to be full-grown,
Who cherished independence, wisely planned,
Was, in that hour, a child lost and alone.

Another child, a small one, takes my hand.
"Show me," he says, "show me my lovely land."
He does not question if I know the way.
The way is something grown-ups understand.

My father, in me, silences dismay,
Rejects excuses, brooks no false delay.
The small one follows, trusting, in his turn,
We journey to a land as bright as day.

And now, I see I have been slow to learn.
My lovely land I finally discern.
Here in the world I meet at every turn,
Here in the child who holds fast to my hand,
Here, oh my father, lies the lovely land.

On Seeing a Leaf House

*   *
*

Are small grave girls still architects with rakes,
Clearing out square green rooms, piling leaf walls,
Inserting, in their proper places, doors
And furniture and narrow joining halls?

Those walls were such that any passer-by
Might have stepped over them from room to room.
Yet, when a caller came, she knocked and I,
Putting by my imaginary broom,

Led her into the parlour where we talked
Of children and the weather, sipped our tea
And smiled at the new wallpaper. And if
An uninvited leaf I then should see

Light in the next room, well within arm's reach
And marring the perfection of the floor,
With what exquisite care I'd rise and go
To fetch it out through the appropriate door.

For My Father

*   *
*

Three weeks ago, they told me you were dead.
My father — gone — and I had never said
How much I loved you, how each hour I cared
That, somewhere in my world, you safely fared.
Between us, talk of love was barbed with wit.
Love was too real for either to admit
Its truth and treat it with solemnity.
We gave our hearts deeply — and laughingly.
And so, I did not say I found in you
A dreamer who went on and dared to do,
A man who fit no pattern ever made,
A clown, a seer, a fighter undismayed
By opposition, once he claimed a cause,
A hero riddled with endearing flaws.
. . . Can you have gone? Have our tomorrows fled
Leaving me burdened with so much unsaid?
Or can I spur my heart till it shall leap
To penetrate this travesty of sleep
And halt Eternity until I tell
How love refused to heed the tolling bell?

I know now why the dazed Ophelia cried
That violets withered when her father died.
When I was told the fact of my like loss,
I saw the bland sky crease and slit across

60

And blow to nothing. Standing wordlessly,
I lost my hold upon reality.
The earth which had, since Genesis, been there
Crumbled, diminished into empty air.
An instant later, it was whole again.
I roused, returned to life, accepted pain,
Faced those who told me and, with tardy pride,
Straightened my spine and resolutely tried
To form a smile. Then, suddenly, I knew
That melodrama would be wrong for you.
Far too distinctly, I could hear your laugh
At any pat or pious epitaph,
Scoffing at every sentimental phrase
Which murdered personality with praise.

We are agreed on that. I will not write
A word I think untrue — or tame — or trite.
And I will stay objective, if I can,
Speaking of you I loved. You were a man
Born with a stubborn caring for your earth.
Finding her poor but with redeeming worth
Hidden beneath her want and ignorance,
You sought to drive her to deliverance.
You planned and preached. You healed and built and taught.
You differed and rebelled, befriended, fought,
Laughed, rescued, ranted . . . angry all your days
Because the pauper seldom strives and pays,
Because the dullard rarely wakes and learns,
Because, of ten cleansed lepers, one returns.

I used to get disgusted with them all,
Using your time at will, sending a call
Whenever trouble touched them, knowing you
Would, grumbling, come and show them what to do.
I wanted you to have the very best
That leisure can provide, good friends and rest
And travel, perhaps, and time for poetry.
But you were never simply left "to be."
Always you had to solve, heal, give, serve, run . . .
And then, before we guessed, your life was done.
"And where was his reward?" I hotly ask.
The answer comes. The prize was in the task.

We need men such as you, men deeply kind,
Able to raise the fallen, lead the blind,
Still pain, deal mightily with needless strife,
Reveal the meanings at the core of life.
I pray they never perish from this earth.
Though you have died, may other men of worth
Keep coming, strong to salvage, strong to fight,
Their lives like beacons in our troubled night.

There — it is said, albeit awkwardly.
I tried to speak of you with honesty.
Yet what was thus accomplished? You are still
Gone from me, and no eulogy can fill
The frightening emptiness your going made.
I miss you so. I know grief should be stayed
By thoughts of Heaven. These fail to comfort me.
I cannot make you fit celestially.

Eternity is spent in praise and prayer.
No one rebels. None causes conflict there.
Such ceaseless peace for you would not suffice.
I see you now — reforming Paradise.

Would they expel you? Or provide you scope
To be yourself? They must have learned to cope.
With nonconformists who have gone before,
John Bunyan must be there and Thomas More,
Cervantes, Wesley, Father Damien,
The Emilys — Carr, Brontë, Dickinson,
Rembrandt, Kagawa, the apostle Paul,
Charles Dickens, Gandhi, William Booth. If all
Of these reside there, Heaven must permit
A place to work, an audience for wit,
A cause to battle for, an inner light,
Friends to be made, and time to paint or write . . .

Is this a valid vision? I think not.
What my grief hungered for, my fancy wrought.
But now I find I do not need this place
To put you. You still occupy the space
In which I walk and think and laugh and move.
Death stilled your heart. It could not touch our love.
This truth will stand undimmed through all my years
And, even now, can check my rising tears.
You are my father still, alive in me.
Love lets me share your immortality.

The Knowing One

*   *
  *

Life will hand Mary
No harder task
Than to know the right answer
And have no one ask.

She Was a Clothier's Daughter

She was a clothier's daughter.
She had a cloak of red
And wide rich skirts of daffodil
And bonnets for her head

Like remnants from a rainbow.
Whenever she went out,
The women ran to windows
And she was talked about.

The village boys brought nosegays.
She dimpled at them all.
But in her heart she waited
To hear a different call.

Then came a stern young preacher.
Sober he was and wise.
He looked at her and did not smile,
But love was in his eyes.

She quite forgot the village boys.
Upon her wedding day,
She walked demurely down the aisle
In gown of simple gray.

Her scarlet cloak, her dress of gold,
She thought no more of these.
With homespun things she packed her box
To sail across the seas.

But on the ship, the other women
Looked at her askance.
For rumor said she used to flirt
And had been known to dance.

They talked of her among themselves
And "Cluck" went every tongue.
And no one thought to comfort her,
So far from home, so young.

When they reached shore, she had no time
To sigh for pretty frocks.
They had to work too hard to tame
This land of stubborn rocks,

This land of want and danger,
Where little children died,
Where everyone wore hodden gray
And no one, ever, cried.

They worked from early morning
Till late into the night,
And wind and water marred the hands
That she had kept so white.

Heavy buckets stooped the back
She once had held so straight,

66

She grew a proper Puritan
In mien and gown and gait.

She loved her husband; yet sometimes
Within her would arise
Such longing for her scarlet cloak
That tears burned in her eyes.

At last, they gathered in the fruit
Of those first months of toil
And seeing the rich harvest they
Had wrested from the soil,

They found that they could face the snows
Without such inner dread,
And gathered at the Meeting House
To praise the Lord for bread.

She sat among them, dressed as they,
Still in her sober gown,
But as they prayed, her gaze went out
Across the hand-hewn town.

She saw the golden sheaves of wheat,
Bronzed fields from whence they came,
The blue-green spruce, the brilliant sky,
The leaves like falling flame.

Her prayer went up belatedly,
A heathen cry apart.
"Oh, thank you for the colors, God,
To feast my hungry heart!"

Homecoming

* *
*

He takes a job as swineherd at the last.
    The scraps he feeds on only hone his hunger.
He watches pigs grow fat. Pride holds him fast
    But it cannot sustain him for much longer.

He gnaws on husks and dreams of food . . . fresh fish,
    Apples, new milk . . . O, comfort me with these!
Here grass is sparse, fields stony. In this land
    There are no lakes to fish, no apple trees.

Then pride lets go. The plenty he once knew,
    The famine he now faces take its place.
He starts the journey home upon the day
    He stops remembering his father's face.

Pared down to bone, he does not pause to plan
    Beyond a platter heaped with meat and bread.
He passes the first landmark. Doggedly,
    He stumbles on and does not lift his head.

His eyes are on the ground. He does not see
    His father running, flying — Gathered in,
Held close against the thunder of that heart,
    The boy feels the familiar war begin.

He pulls back, licks his lips, begins the words,
    "Father, I sinned against both heaven and you.

er's on,
to comb his **hair**,
d Jane Eyre.
Today is gone.

ne's left her book
st for fun,
e in one —
or a hurried look.

ner?" my offspring say,
rslept,
ory kept
ll almost day.

nt, and then they **grin**,
re their power,
for an hour,
orld within.

You need no longer own me as your son —"
    The set speech falters. Wordlessly, the two

Go home together. The boy tastes the tears
    That run unheeded down his father's cheeks.
Where is the man he fought so hard to leave?
    Where is the face that haunted him for weeks?

His father's face is also pared to bone,
    Cleansed of its anger, hollowed, stripped of pride.
The boy sees, painfully, that in the days
    He starved, his father hungered at his side.

He takes the ring, the robes, the dreamed-of feast
    Without the dreaded shame. Grown past surprise,
He finds he cannot rest till he has gone
    Outside to face his brother's sullen eyes.

The elder stands in shadow, will not speak.
    The boy who sought the meeting now turns dumb.
The glib excuses he had planned sound wrong.
    The prayers for pardon now refuse to come.

In desperation, he cries out a name
    Not used since childhood, stammers hoarsely of
Those years before the bitterness began.
    Envy retreats before the power of love.

The father, from the doorway, hears his sons
    Laugh once again, grow close to one another.
He watches them through tears. Perhaps that is why
    He is not sure which is the older brother.

Worlds Within

* *
*

Where are those children? I'm sure I said
That they were to come straight home tonight.
Yet it's nearly five and they're not in sight.
I need him to go to the store for bread.

I've not heard her practice her piece today.
He must finish his speech on Outer Space.
Her dresser drawers are a sheer disgrace.
How will he ever get an A?

The neighbors' children came promptly home,
Why must they be so endlessly good?
Not that I'd swap mine, if I could,
But why did they choose today to roam?

At least, I know where to start to look,
The girl's in the hammock probably,
And my son is perched in the apple tree,
Each poring over a library book.

I have to break in though. It's high time
The speech was finished, the table set,
The homework started . . . and yet . . . and yet . . .
They're lost in a story, caught by a rhyme.

I let them be till th
Then I send Marc
"Put on the pickle
They eat, do home

They're off to bed,
Behind. I am tempt
To pick it up and in
Though I've only t

"Where were you,
I start to snap that
But then I tell them
Me sitting up readi

They gape, for an i
Delighted to learn
To walk away from
And move in a mag

70

"Where's the baby?" she asks. "Is he better today?"
We have no baby here.

"Have you been to church?
I don't hear well, you know,

So I don't go any longer. What was the text?"
But today is Thursday
And texts are out-of-date.

"Is the horse in the stable, Gret? . . .
Who's minding the store, I say? . . .
What's the time? Shouldn't we start for home?"

The poor old thing! Her father had a store
When she was a child.
Somebody tell her the time and quiet her.

No. Listen instead, for a moment.

It is a poem — not pathetic at all!
Listen and hear the echoes
Of work and welcome and a hard-headed warmth
That glow in her words like sparks among the ashes.

When I am old, may my confused speech bear
Witness to a life as worth the living
And may I show such concern
For the ghosts at my elbow.

Tonight I Must Sing

*   *
  *

Tonight I must sing or sob.
Which will it be?
I am balanced between despair
And ecstasy.

Either will leave me hurt.
I shall be torn asunder.
By the tumult of this joy,
This wound of wonder.

If only I could say "No,"
Retreat, refuse,
Bar and bolt my heart —
But one does not choose.

This glory has come from God
(Or is it grief?)
It would be sin in me
To seek relief.

I must sing — or I must cry,
But a cry is a prayer
And when you give in to joy,
The tears are there.

I will both exult and weep.
I will plummet while I soar.

I will die and be born again
Till He asks no more.

I will leap and shout this love.
I will celebrate and sing.
I will go with banners and bells
And trumpeting.

For I choose to sing. I choose!
And the pain that is part of song.
I would praise this light forever —
Though it will not last that long.

You cannot endure such glory.
You are blinded by its flame.
Later on in the darkness,
You give the light a name.

You remember that you were dazzled.
You remember the song you made —
And you sing the strange words over
Because you are grown afraid,

Afraid you will cease to remember
Afraid that the song will die,
Afraid that the vision will vanish
Forever from your sky.

God give me the courage to bear it.
Be near in the coming days.
And God, let me go on singing
While the brightness stays.